# THE ORGANIST'S COLLECTION

## *For Manuals & Pedals*

BOOK NINE : MUSIC FROM
ACROSS THE CENTURIES

We hope you enjoy *The Organist's Collection Book 9*.
Further copies of this and the other books in the series are available
from your local music shop or Christian bookshop.

In case of difficulty, please contact the publisher direct by writing to:

The Sales Department
KEVIN MAYHEW LTD
Rattlesden
Bury St Edmunds
Suffolk  IP30 0SZ

Phone 0449 737978
Fax 0449 737834

Please ask for our complete catalogue of outstanding Church Music.

First published in Great Britain in 1993 by Kevin Mayhew Ltd.

© Copyright 1993 Kevin Mayhew Ltd.

ISBN 0 86209 401 1

Series Music Editor: Joanne Clarke.

Cover illustration by Juliette Clarke.
Printed and bound in Great Britain.

# Contents

# About the Composers

Every musician knows the place and contribution to musical history of composers such as Mendelssohn and Schumann. But what of the others who in their day were valued as fine composers but who are now little known? Below we give a thumbnail sketch of each.

**Thomas Arne** (1710-1778) Leading British composer of his day. Wrote operas, oratorios, keyboard music and songs, including *Rule Britannia*, still sung today.

**Théodore Dubois** (1837-1924) French teacher, composer and organist. He taught at the Paris Conservatoire, later becoming Director there. Prolific composer of music for the stage, concert hall and church.

**Eugène Gigout** (1844-1925) French composer, teacher and organist. He was Professor of Organ at the Paris Conservatoire and renown as a brilliant player.

**Enrique Granados** (1867-1916) Spanish musician who spent the majority of his life in Barcelona teaching at his own Academia Granados. Returning from a concert tour of America, the ship he was on was torpedoed in the English Channel by a German submarine. After being saved by a lifeboat, Granados dived back into the sea to save his wife, but both were drowned.

**Heinrich Hofmann** (1842-1902) German pianist and composer, his best known works are for chamber groups and keyboard.

**Alfred Hollins** (1865-1942) English musician who, despite being blind from birth, became a well-known organist and pianist and a prolific composer of organ music.

**Clément Loret** (1833-1909) French composer, organist and teacher, who studied with Jaak Lemmens.

**Edward MacDowell** (1860-1908) American composer and pianist. Studied at the Conservatories in both Paris and Frankfurt. Injured when knocked down in the street, he suffered mental illness for the rest of his life.

**Johann Rinck** (1770-1846) German organist and composer and a pre-eminent teacher of his day. His works are chiefly for the organ.

**Charles Villiers Stanford** (1852-1924) Irish born composer and organist. Studied at Cambridge University, becoming Organist at Trinity College in 1873. Later he studied in Leipzig and Berlin. Became Professor of Composition at the Royal College of Music where his pupils included Vaughan Williams, Ireland and Holst. Prolific composer of operas and choral music.

# EVENTIDE

## Charles Villiers Stanford (1852-1924)

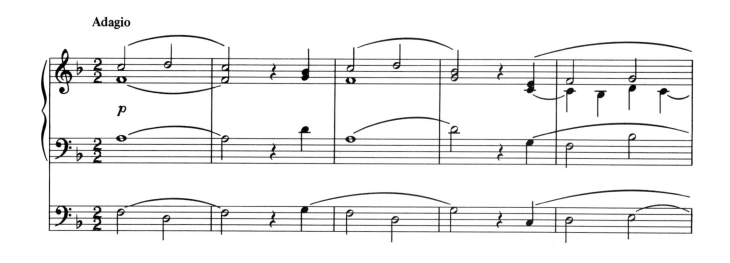

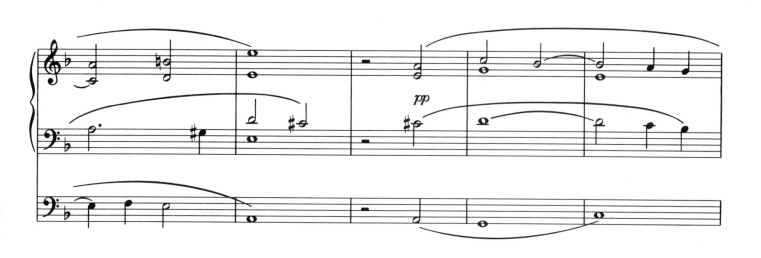

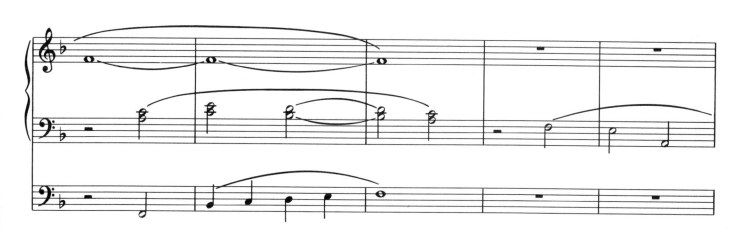

# MEMORIES OF CHILDHOOD

Enrique Granados (1867-1916)
arranged by Colin Hand

**Poco lento**

# THE ROSE GARDEN

Edward MacDowell (1860-1908)
arranged by Colin Hand

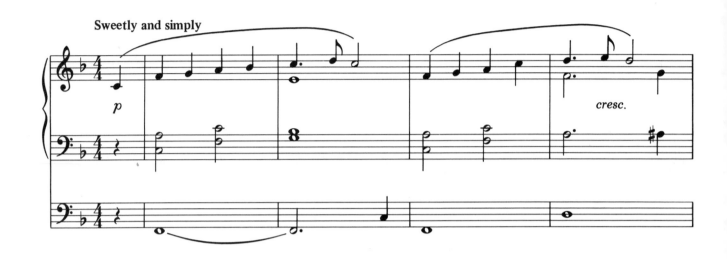

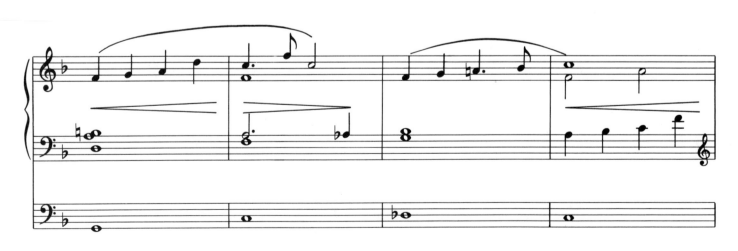

# PRELUDE IN C

Johann Rinck (1770-1846)

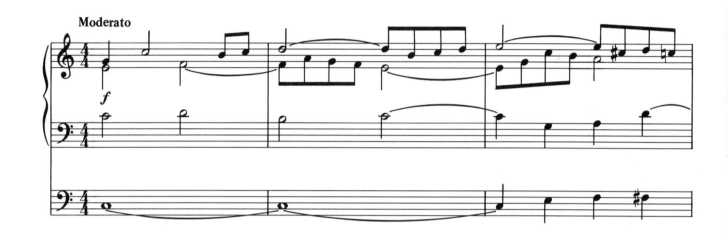

# FINALE

Alfred Hollins (1865-1942)

poco rit.                                                          a tempo

# NOCTURNE

Heinrich Hofmann (1842-1902)
arranged by Colin Hand

**Andante con moto**

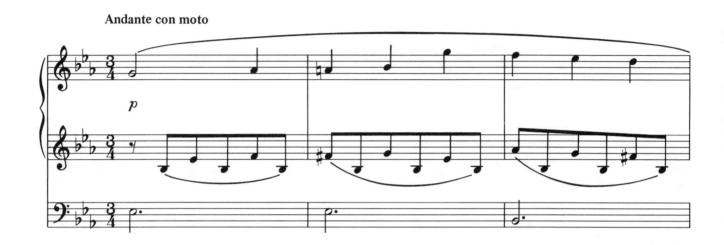

23

# ANDANTE

Johann Rinck (1770-1846)

# MINUET from Sonata No.6

Thomas Arne (1710-1778)
arranged by Colin Hand

# POSTLUDE

Théodore Dubois (1837-1924)

# ADESTE FIDELES

Eugène Gigout (1844-1925)

# DREAMING

Robert Schumann (1810-1856)
arranged by Colin Hand

# ANDANTE CON MOTO

Felix Mendelssohn (1809-1847)
arranged by Colin Hand

**Andante con moto**

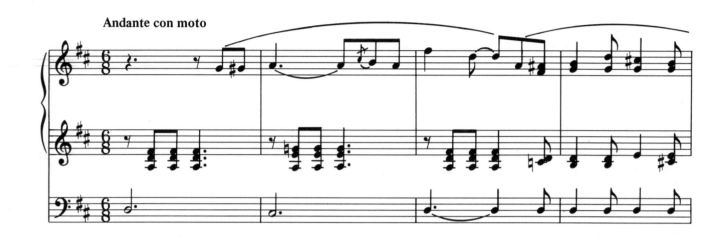

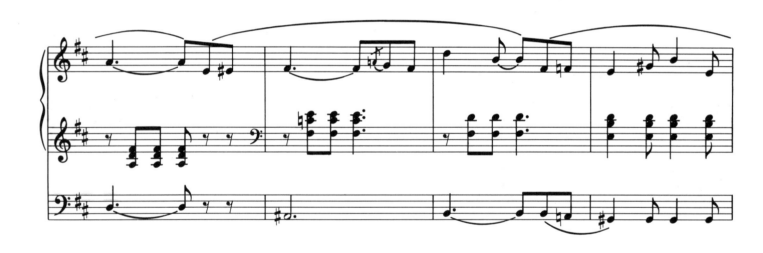

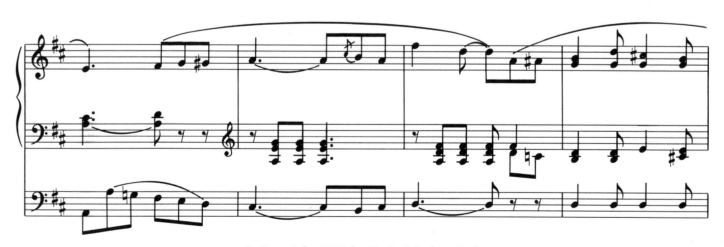

# ETUDE

Clément Loret (1833-1909)

**Allegretto**

# PRELUDE IN E♭

Johann Rinck (1770-1846)